CoComelon™

Annual 2023

Welcome to CoComelon

JJ's waiting for you to come and play!

Write your name or make a scribble, here!

Nice to meet you, ...!

a

Point to the sea horse.

Use a pencil or your finger to trace the letters on the balloons.

Party Pals

Can you help everyone find a friend to take to the party?

Use your finger to follow the trails.

Bella

Cody

Nina

Nico

Mimi

Pepe

Wally

Mochi

Musical Mix-Up

CeCe loves to sing!

See if you can sing the musical scale with your little one. Do, re, mi, fa, sol, la, ti, do!

Boogie on down with CeCe.

Draw lines to put the missing pieces of the musical mat back into place!

Answer on page 76.

Sharing is caring

JJ and TomTom put the gifts under the tree.

Colour the picture.

Can you draw a present here?

Counting cookies

Use a pencil to draw these tasty gingerbread treats for JJ.

Decorate this cookie for YoYo.

How many cookies are there?

3

Answer on page 76.

Meet
CODY

He loves to play all day!

COLOUR IN CODY'S COOL T-SHIRT

TRACE THE WORDS

Cody is JJ's **best** friend. **Choose a game** for them to play.

HE LOVES TO PLAY DINOSAURS. Draw over the dinosaur teeth.

football or reading

Snap!

Peek a boo!

Can you help Cody find the toy hiding in each row?

Point to the toys that are hiding.

1

2

3
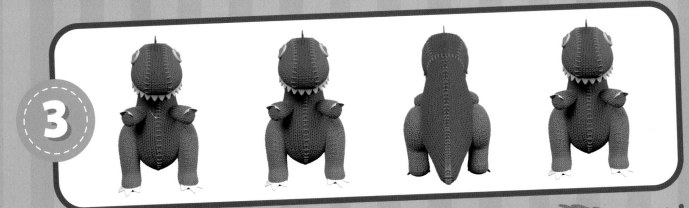

Answers on page 76.

How many!

It's lunch time at Miss Appleberry's nursery.

Count all the...

- Apples
- Carrots
- Strawberries
- Pineapples

A — 3

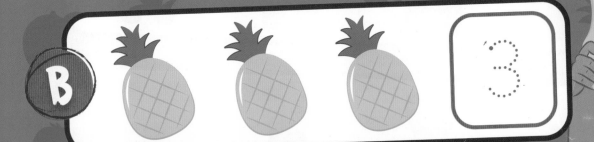

B — 3

C — 5

D — 4

Trace the numbers.

Matching Pairs

Nico is helping tidy the classroom.

Draw lines to match each crayon to its colour partner.

A pair is two of the same thing.

The bathtub song

Splish and splash with Cody!

Can you sing along with the CoComelon friends?

I jump in the bathtub, it's time to get all clean. I'll be the cleanest kid, you've ever seen

SOAP

The soap and the bubbles are filling up the tub So I'll jump in the water and scrub, scrub scrub.

In the bubble bath with my dino, Wash my knees and my toes. In the bubble bath with my dino Wash my knees and toes.

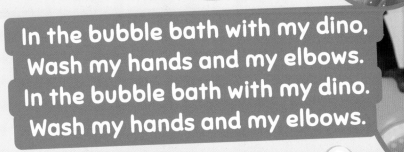

In the bubble bath with my dino,
Wash my hands and my elbows.
In the bubble bath with my dino.
Wash my hands and my elbows.

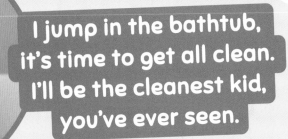

I jump in the bathtub,
it's time to get all clean.
I'll be the cleanest kid,
you've ever seen.

The soap and the bubbles
are filling up the tub.
So I'll jump in the water
and scrub, scrub scrub.

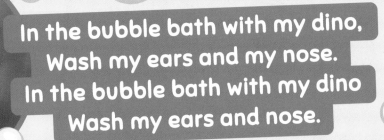

In the bubble bath with my dino,
Wash my ears and my nose.
In the bubble bath with my dino
Wash my ears and nose.

17

Meet JJ!

Say hello to this sweet young man!

JJ LOVES TO FIND OUT ALL ABOUT THE WORLD

WAVE TO JJ!

JJ LOVES HUGS AND FRIENDS.

HE HAS A SWIRLY CURL, RIGHT IN THE MIDDLE OF HIS FOREHEAD.

Draw JJ's curl!

Draw your friend, here.

Well, hello there!

Add some colour so JJ and Cody can play together!

How many shoes can you count?

4

Answer on page 76.

Enough for everyone

It's better when everyone gets a piece of the action!

1 Draw a line so Mum and Dad have 1 piece of doughnut each.

2 Now draw lines so TomTom, JJ and YoYo have a piece of carrot each.

3 Make this orange into 4 pieces. Who will you give each piece to?

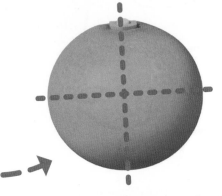

All the colours

Create a colourful **rainbow** for Bella to jump over.

Follow the colour dots with the right coloured pencils, so the **rainbow** matches the unicorn's tail!

21

On the slopes

Let's see what we can spot today.

Point to the...

Star

Hat

Snowman

Snowflakes

Present

Answers on page 76.

Scarf

Miss Appleberry's nursery

It's such fun to play all day.

Colour this square the same colour as Miss Appleberry's sweater.

Can you spot Jellybean the hamster?

How many friends are at nursery today?

 or

24

Write your name or make a scribble on the board.

Help Nina count all the crayons on the table.

CRAYON
CRAYON
CRAYON
CRAYON

MONKEY
SLOTH
LION
FISH
FLAMING
KANGAROO

Mm
Cc

a b c

Beep, beep!

Use a pencil to help the trucks find the way.

Cody needs a helping hand with the trucks.

This truck is driving up and down.

This truck is going round and round.

This one is going over bumps!

Draw a dinosaur

Cody loves to sketch his favourite prehistoric creature!

Draw the other half of this tricky triceratops.

Don't forget to colour everything in orange!

27

Making music

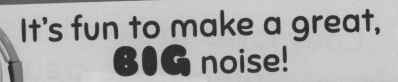

It's fun to make a great, **BIG** noise!

Can you spot the six differences between these two musical pictures?

Tick a box each time you spot a difference.

What's your favourite song?
Can you sing it really loud?

Take off

The friends are counting down.
Can you join in?

Use a pencil to count the rocket down.

Shout out the rocket's countdown!

5

4

3

2

1

30

Blast off!

Seeing shapes

Use a pencil to fill in all the shapes of the Melon Patch Academy!

Finished the shapes? Now colour your picture in!

MELON PATCH ACADEMY

3
2
1

A
B
C

PEEK A BOO!

TIME TO LEARN!

32

CeCe's number search

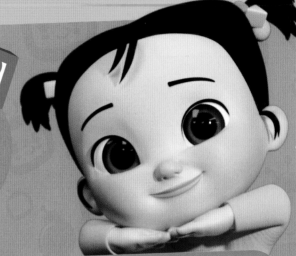

1

3

4

Help CeCe find all the hidden numbers in the picture.

How many...

Dinosaurs

3

Children

2

Trucks

2

3

1

4

All in the family

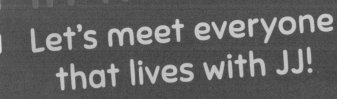

Let's meet everyone that lives with JJ!

Merry Christmas!

JJ

He's the baby of the family.

Mum

She's so kind and helps everyone.

Dad

What a funny guy!

TomTom

He loves to build things and is always trying something new.

YoYo

She is full of fun.

Bingo

Woof, woof! Bingo has so much energy and loves to play!

35

Hi five

The animals are playing with JJ.

Trace the outlines of each character with a pencil, then colour everyone in!

Time to eat

Nina is hungry! Draw her something to munch.

Will you draw...

Waffles?

Yoghurt?

Fruit?

Or something else?

Night night, everyone

It's time to say goodnight!

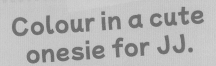
Colour in a cute onesie for JJ.

JJ's onesie!

The children are waiting for a bedtime story. Can you point to their book?

DINOSAURS

Say "night, night, JJ!"

sweet
dreams

Close your eyes and
pretend to go to sleep.

Splash-splash

Let's get clean!

See if you can find all the things JJ and TomTom need for their bath!

- sponge
- brush
- toy boat
- duck

Use your finger to **pop** the bubbles in order from 1-5.

1
2
3
4
5

starry starry night!

Join the dots so JJ can look at the night sky.

Twinkle twinkle little stars!

1 2 3 4 5 6 7 8 9

3 2 4 5

1 2 3 4 5

1 2 3 4 5

How many stars can you see? Write your answer in the box.

3

Rise and shine!

Brrr. It's cold outside. Help CeCe get ready to play with her friends in the snow.

1 Scribble inside the boxes next to the things CeCe should wear in the cold weather.

a

b

c

d

2 Draw lines to link the matching winter hats.

3 CeCe and her friends need help with their outfits. Read the instructions, then draw what is needed.

Draw CeCe's hat.

Draw TomTom's boots.

Draw JJ's scarf.

Ask a grown-up to time how long it takes you to put on your coat and hat!

Answers on page 77.

YoYo's challenge chart!

How many of these fun things can you do?

How to use your challenge chart

1. Every day choose a challenge.
2. When you've done your best to complete the challenge, tick it off.
3. How many challenges can you complete?

Draw or paint the biggest picture that you can make of your favourite toy!

Have some quiet time. Look out of a window. What can you see happening outside?

Go outside and see how many animals you can spot? Look in the sky, under rocks, anywhere and everywhere!

Choose your favourite book and try reading it out loud.

44

Pretend to be a big, scary dinosaur. How loudly can you roar?

How many different kinds of fruit can you think of? Draw a picture of the yummiest one.

Make up a funny face and see if you can make everyone laugh.

Try eating a new food today. Try and describe the taste and smell to your grown-up.

Great job!

....

has completed YoYo's challenge!

45

Let's play!

JJ and Bingo are playing doctors.
Join in the fun!

Circle your answer.

1 Who is Mum standing next to?

YoYo   or   JJ

Can you stick out your tongue and say, "**ahhh!**", just like Bingo?

Look at these little pictures.

Can you spot them in the big picture?

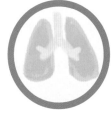 

Colour in a shape when you spot each one.

2 How many books can you count on the small table?

Write the number in the box.

Super fast!

Whoosh! The friends are seeing how fast they can run.

Draw over the dotted lines to go running with your CoComelon friends.

Next time you're outside see how fast you can run!

Friends forever!

Colour in JJ and Cody as they head off to school.

Use this little picture to help you.

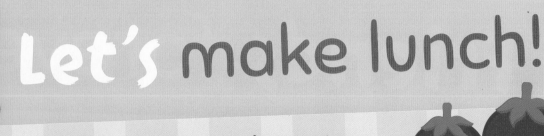

Let's make lunch!

Help JJ learn how to make a pizza for lunch.

Start

1
Follow the path with your finger, and finish the activities as you go.

2
Draw lines over the dough to knead it. This is the pizza base.

3
Trace over the spiral line with a red crayon to swirl on the tomato sauce.

4
Draw short yellow lines to add cheese to your pizza.

50

6

Great job. You've learnt how to make pizza. Rub your tummy and say, "**Yummy!**"

5

Draw lines to add the toppings you like onto the pizza.

That looks great!

Let's all have some pizza!

The lunch song

What yummy food will we find in our lunchboxes today?

I've got something in my lunchbox,
Something yummy I know.
I've got something in my lunchbox,
It's lunchtime now, let's go.

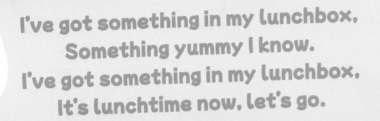

I've got chicken nuggets, carrot sticks,
Grapes and some potato crisps.
Chicken nuggets carrot sticks,
Grapes, potato crisps.

I've got something in my lunchbox,
Something yummy, I know.
I've got something in my lunchbox,
It's lunchtime now, let's go.

I've got tortillas with some rice and beans,
Salsa and some leafy greens.
Tortillas with some rice and beans,
Salsa, leafy greens.

I've got something in my lunchbox,
Something yummy, I know.
I've got something in my lunchbox,
It's lunchtime now, let's go.

I've got pasta with tomato sauce,
Bread and salad that's been tossed.
Pasta with tomato sauce,
Bread and salad tossed.

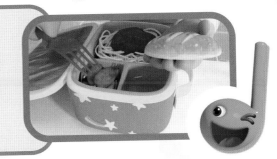

I've got something in my lunchbox,
Something yummy, I know.
I've got something in my lunchbox,
It's lunchtime now, let's go.

I've got chicken dumplings with some rice,
Veggies that taste very nice.
Chicken dumplings with some rice,
Veggies very nice.

I've got something in my lunchbox,
Something yummy, I know.
I've got something in my lunchbox,
It's lunchtime now, let's go.

I've got a sandwich made with
ham and cheese,
Broccoli and apples, please.
Sandwich made with ham and cheese,
Broccoli, apples, please.

What would you like to
have in your lunchbox?
Tell your grown-up.

Let's write!

Can you write a, b, c with JJ and CeCe?

a is for apple

b is for banana

c is for crayon

Great job! Can you write the letter your first name begins with?

. . . .

Rainy day

Can you work out who's who through the rain?

Circle your answers!

1  Is it JJ or TomTom?

2  Is it Bella or Nina?

3  Is it Jellybean or Bingo?

4  Is it Miss Appleberry or Mum?

Answers on page 77.

The ant and the grasshopper

1 One hot day, a grasshopper sat on a blade of grass enjoying the sunshine.

"What a lovely day!" he yawned, looking around happily. The grasshopper spent the whole morning eating grass until he was full.

2 "Right, I think I'll make some music," he said, hopping onto a mushroom. The grasshopper picked up his violin and started playing.

3 "Please stop making that noise," said an ant, who was dragging a huge piece of corn. "I'm trying to work, and you're giving me a headache."

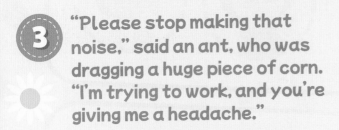

4 "What are you doing?" asked the grasshopper. "We're getting food ready for the winter." said the ant, pointing to his ant friends who were all busy carrying food to their ant hill.

5 "But winter is ages away," said the grasshopper. "Playing is so much more fun than working."

"I can't," said the ant. "I've got too much to do."

Playing is so much more fun.

I've got too much to do.

6 "What a silly creature!" said the grasshopper, closing his eyes for a nap.

The ants carried on working all the way through the autumn, making sure their home was cosy and warm and full of food.

Meanwhile, the grasshopper lazed around, playing his music and having fun.

7 "Why don't you store food for winter?" asked the ant.

"I'm too busy having fun," said the grasshopper. "Winter's ages away."

8 Time passed, and along came the winter. The grasshopper was cold. Too cold to hop. Too cold to make his music.

He headed up to the ant hill and knocked on the door.

9 "It's so cold," the grasshopper shivered. "And I've nothing to eat."

"It's nice and warm in our nest," said the ant, holding the door open. "Come inside."

Mmmm, thank you. ♡

10 "We've got loads to eat," said the ant, giving the grasshopper a huge bowl of yummy, warm soup. "Enough to see us through to spring."
The grasshopper tucked in happily. "From now on, I'll make sure work comes before play," he said.

I can do it!

JJ and his friends are playing Let's Pretend. Join in the fun.

1 JJ is pretending to be an artist. Help him draw a lovely picture.

2 CeCe is a builder. Circle the odd builder's hat out.

a b c

3 Nico is a firefighter. Trace over the hose so he can can get water to the fire.

4 Cody is an astronaut. Colour in his rocket. Use the dots to help you.

Do you know the name of our planet?

Share the love!

Finish drawing this picture of JJ, then colour it in.

Hands up!

Can you place your hand on the page below and draw round it?

What a great picture!

Write your name here! ....

Let's move!

Move around the room with the animal friends!

Pretend to lick your paws like a cat!

Do each move, then colour in your **Cocomelon** animal friends.

Look up at the moon, and howl like a wolf!

Crawl like a bear. Don't forget to growl.

Oink like a pig and sniff the ground looking for food.

Pretend to swing from tree to tree like a monkey.

Sway your trunk from side to side like an elephant.

Squeak like a mouse, then pretend to nibble some cheese.

Can you pretend to be any other animals?

A helping hand!

Your CoComelon friends need you.

1 JJ has lost his lunchbox. Shout, "Found you!", when you spot it.

2 Cody is playing dress-up. Join the dots to see what he's dressed as.

1 2 3 4 5 6 7 8 9 10 11 12

3

TomTom is helping put the shopping away. Draw lines to match the food into pairs.

A pair is two of the same thing.

How many pairs did you count? 3

4

Bella is sorting the pens for Miss Appleberry. Scribble over the yellow pens.

Baa baa black sheep

It's bath time for the sheep!
Join in with the nursery rhyme
as JJ tries to catch him!

1

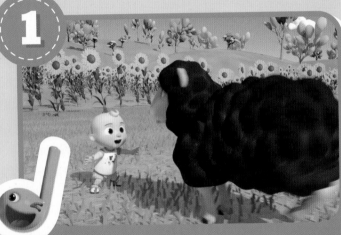

Baa baa black sheep,
have you any wool?
Yes sir, yes sir, three
bags full.

One for the master,
one for the dame,
one for the little boy
who lives down
the lane.

Baa baa black sheep,
have you any wool?
Yes sir, yes sir, three
bags full.

2

Baa baa blue sheep,
have you any wool?
Yes sir, yes sir, three
bags full.

One for the master,
one for the dame,
one for the little boy
who lives down
the lane.

Baa baa blue sheep,
have you any wool?
Yes sir, yes sir, three
bags full.

3

Baa baa pink sheep, have you any wool? Yes sir, yes sir, three bags full.

One for the master, one for the dame, one for the little boy who lives down the lane.

Baa baa pink sheep, have you any wool? Yes sir, yes sir, three bags full.

4

Baa baa white sheep, have you any wool? Yes sir, yes sir, three bags full.

One for the master, one for the dame, one for the little boy who lives down the lane.

Baa baa white sheep, have you any wool? Yes sir, yes sir, three bags full.

Make a play scene
Have lots of pop-up fun with JJ and his family.

Ask your grown-up to help you with the cutting out.

Instructions

- Ask your grown-up to photocopy or scan and print these pages if you don't want to cut up your book.

- Cut out and stick everything to thin card. Fold along the dotted lines and stand up!

FOLD

© Moonbug

FOLD

© Moonbug

FOLD

© Moonbug

FOLD

© Moonbug

© Moonbug

© Moonbug

FOLD

Grow and bloom!

Add some colour, so JJ can make his garden grow.

Spring
HAPPY

Fruity fun

JJ can't wait to eat all these yummy summer fruits.

Point to the fruit, you'd most like to eat.

Circle the one that comes next in each row.

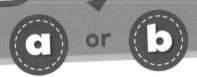

1

   **a**  or **b**

2

   **a**  or **b**

3

    **a**  or **b**

Answers on page 77.

Brilliant birthday

YoYo is having a birthday party. Count and spot everything in the picture.

Tick when you spot these things.

1 Birthday cake

2 Birthday banner

3 Birthday hats

4 Balloons

5 Presents

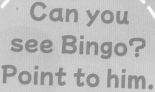

Can you see Bingo? Point to him.

Do you know when your BIRTHDAY is?

Sing, 'Happy Birthday!' to YoYo and pretend to blow out the candles on her cake.

Answers on page 77.

73

Hide and seek!

Can you spot who's hiding from TomTom at the beach?

Colour in your answer.

1

Is it CeCe or Bella?

2

Is it Nico or YoYo?

3

Is it Nina or JJ?

Good dog!

Help Bingo find his way through the maze to JJ.

How many bones did you collect?

4

start

finish

Answers

Page 6–7

Page 8

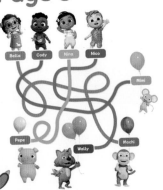

Page 9

Page 11

There are 3 cookies.

Page 13

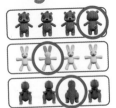

Page 14

A – 3, B – 3, C – 5, D – 4.

Page 15

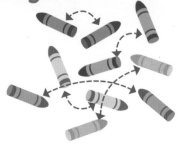

Page 19

There are 4 shoes.

Page 22–23

Page 24–25

There are 4 friends at nursery.
Jellybean is behind Bella.
There are 4 crayons on the table.

Page 28–29

Page 33

There are 3 dinosaurs.
There are 2 children.
There are 2 trucks.

Page 40

Page 41

There are 3 stars.

Page 42–43

1 – b and c.

2 –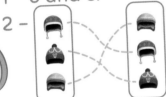

Page 46–47

1 – YoYo is standing next
to mum.
2 – There are 3 books
on the table.

Page 55

1 – JJ.
2 – Nina.
3 – Jellybean.
4 – Miss Appleberry.

Page 58–59

2 – c.
4 – Earth is the
name of our planet.

Page 64–65

1 –

3 – There are 3 pairs.

Page 71

1 – a, 2 – b, 3 – a.

Page 72–73

Page 74

1 – Bella, 2 – Nico, 3 – JJ.

Page 75

There are 4 bones.

Well
done!